I TA
TO CATS

I TALK TO CATS

by Annie Lawson

A Deirdre McDonald Book

London

First published in 1995
by Deirdre McDonald Books
128 Lower Richmond Road
London SW15 1LN

ISBN 1 898094 05 5

Printed in Great Britain by
Redwood Books

SHOPPING for CATS

True Story

When I was a little girl, we got a cat called Mitten...

True Story

When I was a little girl, we got a cat called Mitten...

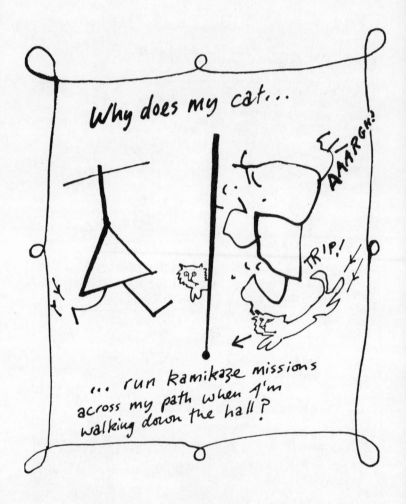

The Woman who loved Cats Too Much.

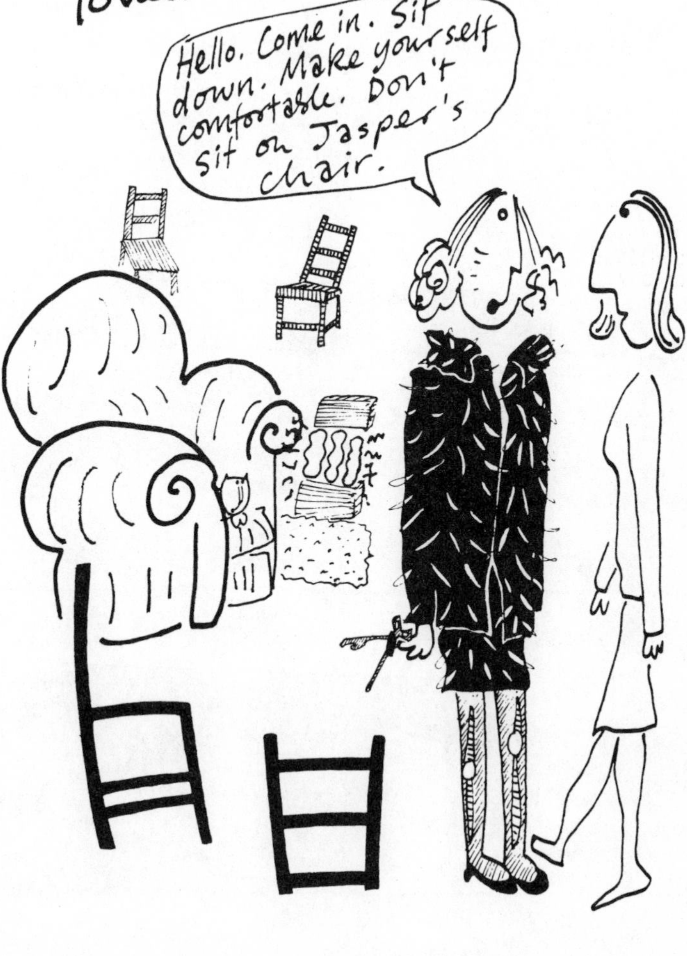

A CAT'S LIFE

THE CAT'S DINNER

Thanks to Nick

True Story

When I was a little girl, we had a cat called Mitten...

True Story

When I was a little girl, we had a cat called Mitten.

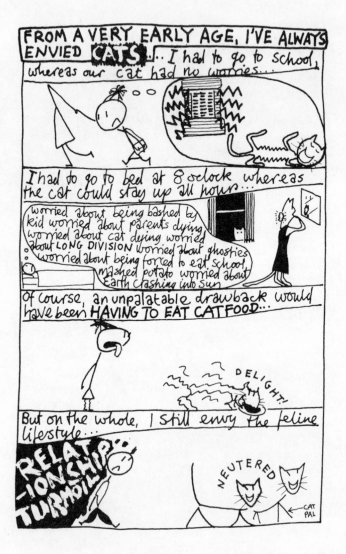

CONT. →

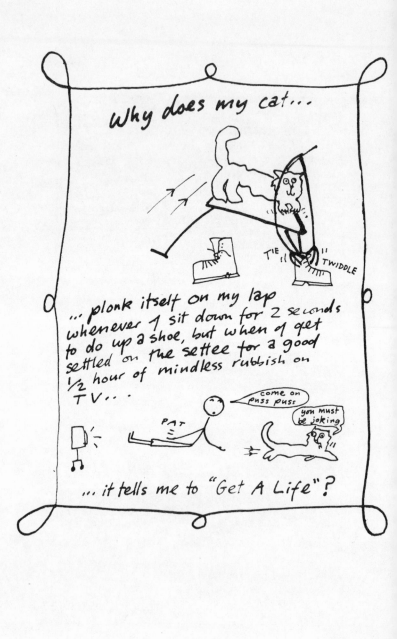

Teach Your
Cat To Read
HEMINGWAY.

ASK NOT FOR WHOM THE CAT FLAPS

IT FLAPS FOR THEE.

Real life
Catastrophe

THE COUPLE WHO IN IRONIC SPIRIT NAMED THEIR CAT "HERPES"

(... BECAUSE ONCE YOU'D GOT IT, IT WAS THE DEVIL TO GET RID OF...) WHO THEN WENT AND LOST IT IN AN UNDERGROUND CARPARK.

HAVE YOU BEEN HERE? YOU'VE JUST EMERGED FROM A LOVING AND MUTUALLY SUPPORTIVE INTERACTION WITH SOMEONE WHO HAS MET YOUR NEEDS (AND HOPEFULLY, YOU THEIRS) FOR A CONSIDERABLE PERIOD OF TIME (WELL, IT WASN'T PERFECT, BUT WHAT IS?), AND NOW YOU'VE BROKEN UP.

Teach Your Cat
To Read
VIRGINIA WOOLF.

"Women have served all these centuries as looking glasses possessing the magic and delicious power of reflecting the figure of ~~the man~~ THE CAT at 100 times his natural size."

Animal Passion

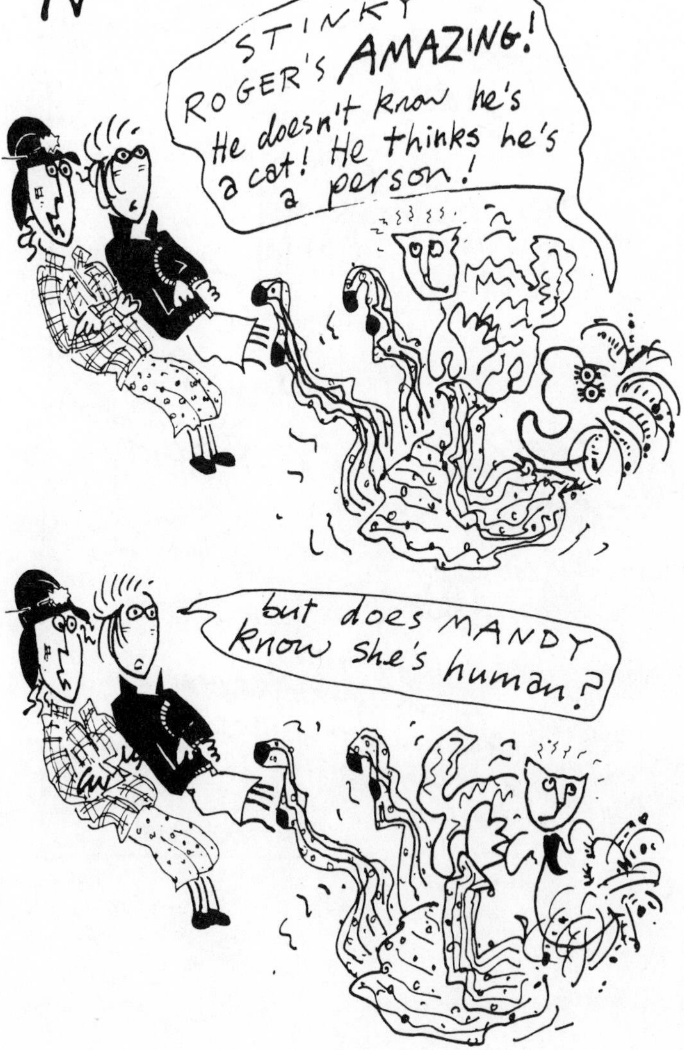

Teach Your Cat
To Read
J. B. PRIESTLEY.

IT IS HARD
TO TELL WHERE
MOULDERING
CHICKEN
CARCASS
ENDS AND
GOD
BEGINS.

True Story

When I was a little girl, we had a cat called Mitten.

True Story

When I was a little girl, we had a cat called Mitten.

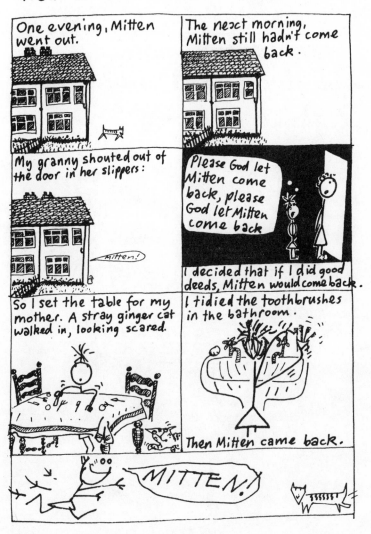

True Story

When I was a little girl, we had a cat called Mitten.

*　　　*　　　*

It was my abiding fantasy that one day Mitten would get up on her hind legs and walk...

and talk...

Teach Your Cat To Read
FE~~X~~^LINISM

THE FE
EU VO
THE FE
MYSTIQU
AGAINS
OUR WIL

BACKLASH

We were discussing the possibility of making one of our cats Pope, recently, and we decided that the fact that she was not Italian, and was female, made the third point that she was a cat, quite irrelevant.

KATHARINE WHITEHORN

Sophie's Story

Teach Your Cat
To Read
D. H. LAWRENCE.

"Ours is an essentially tragic
age but we refuse emphatically to
take it tragically.
"This was Constance The Cat's
position."

Real life
Catastrophe

THE GROWN MAN WHOSE CAT FOLLOWED HIM TO WORK THROUGH THE PARK.

Teach Your Cat To Read SHAKESPEARE.

"Is this A CAN-OPENER A see before me?"

Teach Your Cat
To Read

HENRY MILLER.

"~~sex~~ <u>sleep</u> is one of the nine reasons for reincarnation... The other eight are unimportant."

NAKED PASSIONS

Teach Your Cat
To Read
SYLVIA PLATH.

Pussy-Madness

True Story

When I was a little girl, we had a cat called Mitten...

My best friend was Mitten.

But Mitten had a contender: Susan Staniland.

One night, I was running round in circles on the front lawn:

Suddenly:

Hello, I'm Susan. Can I play with you?

THINKS: NO.

yes all right

We carried on with the game, stiffly.

Then we did turnovers on the swing. She was from Lancashire. She had a strange accent.

Her father worked for a soap company. His job was teaching people how to sell Omo. They never spent more than two years in one place.

They lived in a new house behind ours. The plaster was so new it couldn't be wallpapered.

Susan Staniland and I were best friends for two years. Although, when they moved on (never having finished decorating) to a new soap posting, I didn't fret.

"The Cat Who Walked By Himself" was my romanticised ideal.

ALONE

True Story

When I was a little girl, we had a cat called Mitten...

True Story

When I was a little girl, we had a cat called Mitten...

Mitten was central to my life...

...as was Home decorating.

Once, we went to Mother Shipton's Petrifying Well at Knaresborough.

HAT TURNED TO STONE

STUFFED TOY TURNED TO STONE

You put your hand in a pool of water in the cave wall and made a wish.

I WISH TO HAVE HAD MY BEDROOM DECORATED BY OCT. **th (MY BIRTHDAY)

I got my wish...

... but the wallpaper didn't extend to the full wall, so two unpapered patches were left behind the bedheads.

It was bad enough having to have the spare bed in my room, without having unpapered patches behind the bedheads, but the situation was un-negotiable.

The picture rails had had to come down.

OBVIOUS MARKS WHERE PICTURE RAILS ONCE WERE.

The wallpaper was dark green with rows of white flamingos.

Two walls were painted pastel green, one pastel blue and the wall behind the beds was papered (barring behind the bedheads).

There was no paper behind the bedheads. It didn't notice, as long as the beds stayed put.

MIAOW MIAOW MIAOW MIAOW!
TRANSLATION: LITTER-TRAY...CAT PLOP... PET POO
TREAD-PRUF GRANULES...TOM CAT STINK...

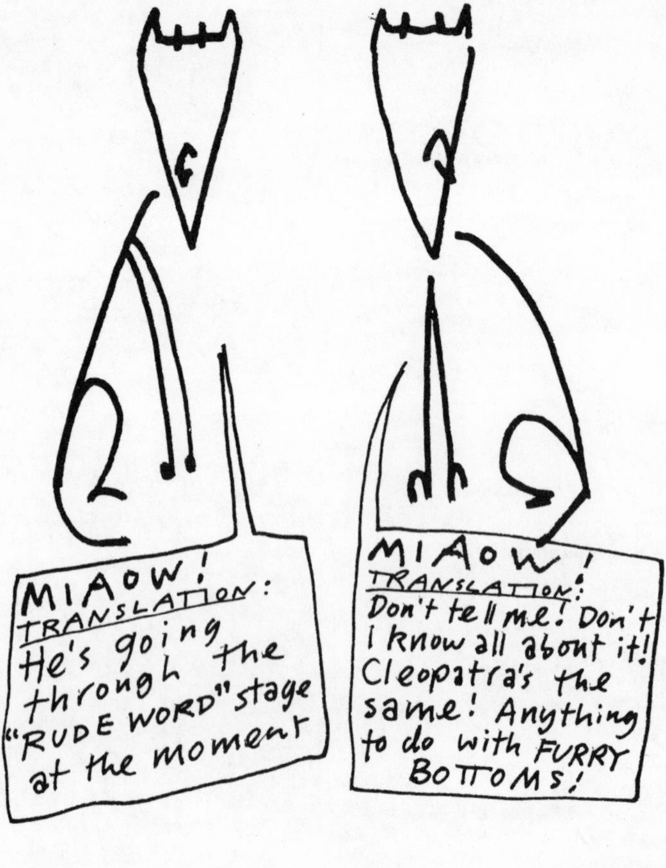
MIAOW! TRANSLATION: He's going through the "RUDE WORD" stage at the moment
MIAOW! TRANSLATION: Don't tell me! Don't I know all about it! Cleopatra's the same! Anything to do with FURRY BOTTOMS!

Teach Your Cat To Read
SELF-HELP MANUALS

IT'S A SAD CAT THAT BUYS ITS OWN CATNIP.

PUSSIES WHO LOVE TOO MUCH

A House of Cats

A House of Cats

A House of Cats

A House of Cats

A House of Cats

...because we ALREADY HAVE A TORTOISESHELL CAT, which APPARENTLY IS A VERY JEALOUS TYPE...

...that would certainly ATTACK AND KILL A NEWCOMER CAT...

It's funny they said that though... because she doesn't fight those strays...

... so we heard about this WOMAN IN WOOLWICH who keeps A HOUSE FULL OF HOMELESS CATS...

DING DONG

... whose REGULATIONS might be LESS STRINGENT than the "F-A-C-A-H S".

WE WANT TO ADOPT A HOMELESS CAT

I'M SORRY CHUCKS. I HAVEN'T ANY CATS.

A House of Cats

A House of Cats

***rgh!
... IT'S THE TEENAGE MUTANT MIDDLECLASS DAUGHTERS!
MUMMY
***rgh!
tra la!
***rgh! HONESTLY, MUMMY!
SAD SHOES
SAD SKIRT
SAD JUMPER
SAD EARRINGS
SAD HAIRCUT
MUMMY LOOKS LIKE SOMETHING THE CAT DRAGGED IN.

Real life
Catastrophe

THE COUPLE, WHO BEFORE GOING ON HOLIDAY FIXED THEIR CATFLAP SO THAT IT ONLY LET THE CATS THROUGH ONE WAY...

UNFORTUNATELY, THEY SET IT TO "IN ONLY"

AND ARRIVED BACK TO A HOUSE
FULL OF STRANGE CATS...

... AND DISTRAUGHT NEIGHBOURS.

True Story

When I was a little girl, we had a cat called Mitten...

Mitten would lie on the sheepskin rug in front of the electric fire.

... and there was a small orange crescent of scorched wool along the straight edge...

The rug was ½ moon-shaped.

...in front of the electric fire which had "coal-effect".

(... in this respect differing from Aunty Mollie's one which had "log-effect.") An impression of glowing embers was created from inside the workings by means of a red lightbulb propelling a fan above it by convection...

...except that we didn't spend money on a coloured lightbulb. Instead, my father painted an ordinary one with poster paint.

INTENT

RED

But the heat of the bulb would immediately burn the poster paint off, rendering the artificial embers unhappily anaemic.

100 WATT

I kept him at that lightbulb.

DADDY!!! IT'S TIME TO PAINT THE BULB AGAIN DADDY!!!

HOW I LOATHED THAT TOO-PALE FLICKERING.

True Story

When I was a little girl, we had a cat called Mitten.